A companion volume by the same author: The Discovery of the Circle

DISCOVERY OF THE SQUARE

BRUNO MUNARI

GEORGE WITTENBORN INC.
1018 MADISON AVENUE, NEW YORK 21, N.Y.

nature in many minerals. According to Peano it is a curve. It can be transformed into triangles or rectangles simply by appropriate cuts and rearrangements. In ancient times it had the power of warding off plagues. It has given form both to famous ancient cities and to modern buildings: Babylon, Tell el Amarna, the Parthenon, the Arch of Septimius Severus, the Duomo of Pisa, Palazzo Farnese, Le Corbusier's museum of unlimited extendability... The bays of the portico of Brunelleschi's Foundling Hospital are square. In the ground-plans of many churches the square area below is the most logical answer to the hemispherical dome above, just as a square photograph corresponds, with the minimum distortion or waste, to the round lens of the camera. Phidias used a square form for his lacunaria. At Olympia, the Palestra, the Theocoleon, the Leonidaeum and other buildings had square ground plans...

Many ancient games still in use today are based on the square: chess, checkers, the fifteen puzzle with its ten trillion possible combinations, dice, even puss in the corner... And the cowboy square dances are famous.

In the Eastern Chin dynasty it gave the Chinese written character its square form. It has given structure to the letters of our own, of the Hebrew and other alphabets. All over the world, a small square of linen is a handkerchief. Two squares of matting are the basic unit of the traditional Japanese house. Twenty-eight squares cover the surface of a brick. According to an old Chinese saying the infinite is a square without angles.

" The square is the purest form of a spatial idea complete in itself. It represents one of the orders of pregnant spiritual symbolism. All other rectangles are squares which depart from the norm by the extension of height or width. "

square is as high and as wide as a man his arms outstretched. In the most ant writings, and in the rock inscriptions early man, it signifies the idea of enure, of house, of settlement.

gmatic in its simplicity, in the monotous repetition of four equal sides and equal angles, it creates a series of inteng figures: a whole group of harmonic angles, the golden section, and the logamic spiral, which also occurs in nature in organic growth of plants and in parts of nals.

h its structural possibilities it has helpartists and architects of all epochs and es by giving them a harmonic skeleton which to build an artistic construction. s therefore present in all styles of all ples in all periods, both as a structural nent and as a surface to support and rmine a particular form of decoration. s static if it stands on its side and dyic if it stands on an angle. It is magic lled with numbers, and it can also be olic and satanic if these numbers maintheir relationship no matter whether are squared or cubed. It is found in

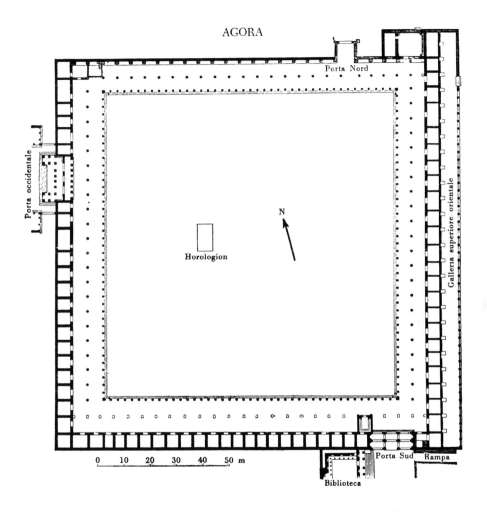

Plan of the Agora of Ephesus, Hellenistic age.

JOSEF ALBERS

Homage to the twilight square, 1951.

AAGARD ANDERSEN

Design in black and white on an area of 48 squares.

THE ALTAR OF BURNT OFFERING

" And thou shalt make an altar of shittim wood, five cubits long, and five cubits broad: the altar shall be foursquare... " - Exodus xxvii. 1.

8

racters from American petroglyphs at gutà.

CIENT EGYPT

, in ancient Egypt, was based on geory and the fixed rules of a canon. The s of this system was the square. Since time of the Old Kingdom, as may be

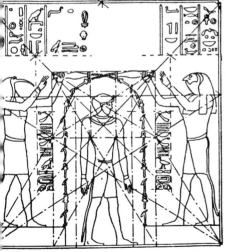

n in the tomb of King Zoser of the third asty, at Sakkara, artists who had a wall

to decorate divided it up into squares so as to be able to calculate the proportions. Traces of similar grid-lines have also been found in other tombs at Sakkara, and in tombs of the New Kingdom at Thebes. In sculpture the square form inspired the so-called " cubic " statue in which the human figure, generally a person of rank, is disposed in such a way that it remains within the co-ordinates of a cube. A typical example is the statue of the architect Senmut of the eighteenth dynasty, in the Cairo Museum.

The square is the basis of the pyramid and, in Gnostic times, mystical and symbolical interpretations in connection with this geometric shape were disseminated. In fact, the square with its four sides, was regarded as the symbol of the four elements and thus of " materiality ", subordinate to the form of the triangle, whose three sides symbolized the spirit, and also represented, schematically, the rising flame: *pyra*, fire, whence " *pyramid* ".

THE KITE

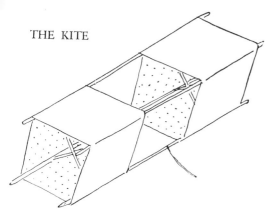

A box-kite of two simple cells.

THE ROMAN ARCH

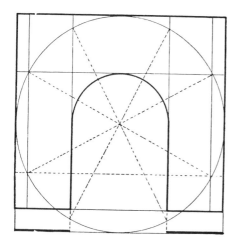

Proportions of the Arch of Septimius Severus.

MAYAN ARCHITECTURE

Detail of a frieze of the temple of Ux[...] in Yucatán. All Mayan buildings are ba[...] on mathematical laws, on precise forms [...] proportions.

‹LON

...on is a square city, says Herodotus,
...every side measures one hundred and
...y stadia. The city is full of three-
...ur-story houses, and is traversed by
...ht parallel streets perpendicular to the
... It is also divided into two parts: in
...art is the Royal Palace, and in the
... part the bronze-doored sanctuary of
...he Babylonian Zeus, two stadia square.
...e middle of the sanctuary a mas-
...ower rises on a square base, each side
...ich measures one stadium. This tower
...rts other towers, one on top of the
... in decreasing order, eight in all. On
...ast tower there is a great temple and
...there is an elaborately ornamented bed
...a gold table beside it. No deity and
...man being lives in this place, except
...oman chosen by the god.

...MIOM

...nin character. Phonetic value: ba. The
... sign has, in Korean, the phonetic
...: miom.

...ian hieroglyphs. Phonetic value: bet.

GREEK BAS-RELIEF

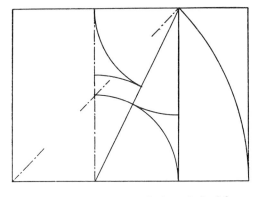

Proportions of a Greek bas-relief. Athens.

11

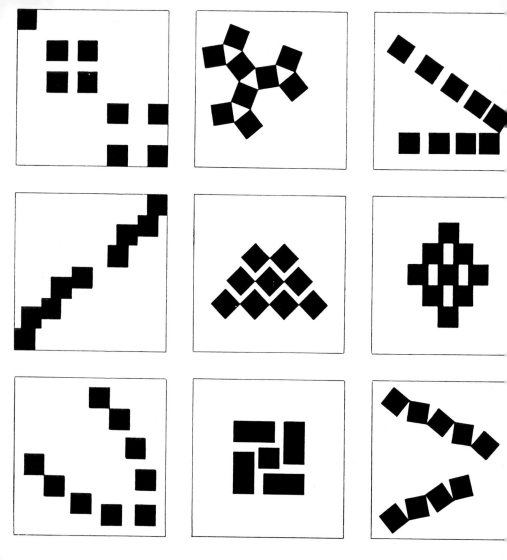

AL-SHAMIN

onometric view of the monumental build-
s of the Temple of Baal-shamin at Pal-
ra (reconstructed).

LLOLI

   field
are
   square
are
   city
are
   prison
are
   tomb
are
   tent
are
   skin
are
   pupil
are
   square

iety.

m poems on elementary geometry, Basle
59.

THE BAUHAUS

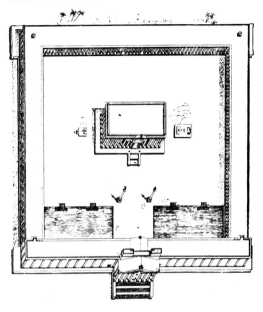

Experiments with different groupings of
nine squares. The Bauhaus, Weimar.

MAX BILL

Field with eight groups, 1956.

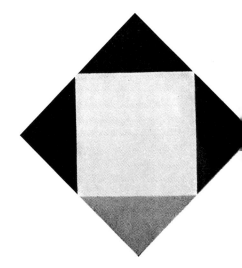

White element, oil on canvas, 68 by 68 cm (26 ¾ by 26 ¾ in.), diagonal.

MOUTH

Chinese ideogram meaning "mouth".

HOUSE

The word "house" in Sumerian ideographic writing.

MASUZAWA'S HOUSE

The house of the architect Masuzawa in Tokyo, 1952.

GOTHIC CATHEDRAL

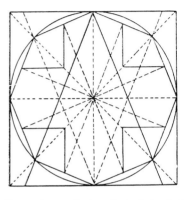

Proportions of the Cathedral of Chalons sur-Marne. Cross-section.

ELECTRONIC BRAIN

THE CHURCH OF SANTA SOPHIA

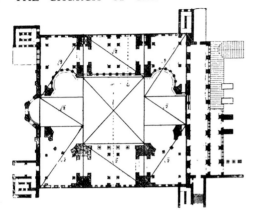

Santa Sophia, Constantinople. The plan consists of rectangles of proportions 1 : √2 arranged around a central area which is very nearly a square.

THE CHURCH OF SAN LORENZ

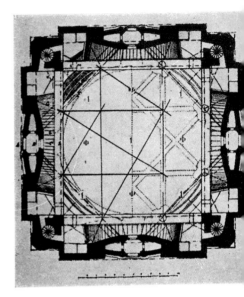

The church of San Lorenzo in Turin, Guarino Guarini. The whole composition based on a square divided in turn into squares and golden rectangles.

FIVE TIMES

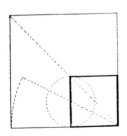

Given a square, describe another square five times larger.

SHELLS

The organic growth of many shells follow the curve of the logarithmic spiral, which derives from the square.

COMPOSITIONS

Composition with four squares.

Composition with eight squares.

CONCAVE CONVEX

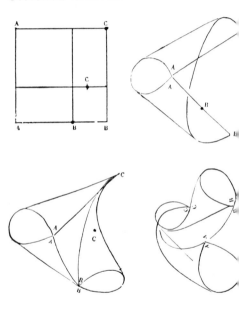

Form obtained by bending a square of wire gauze until the corners touch at pre-established points on the surface. The explanatory diagrams show the various stages in the production of the final form. The points of anchorage are established on the surface of the square according to harmonic

rtions. These wire gauzes, so curved
hung from the ceiling of a room, may
sed to decorate a wall, their mobile
ransparent shadows giving a fish-net ef-
Munari, 1948.

SOLAR ENERGY CONCENTRATOR

The above concentrator is used in America to harness solar energy. It consists of 180 adjustable mirrors, each about 50 cm. square.

AGAINST THE PLAGUE

In ancient times the square was believed have magical properties including power prevent plague, and it was common pract to wear a silver disk, with a square cut it, on a necklace.

ROMANESQUE CROSS

Notre-Dame-du-Port, Clermont-Ferrand, venth century.

CRETE

Characters from a Minoan inscription, Cre

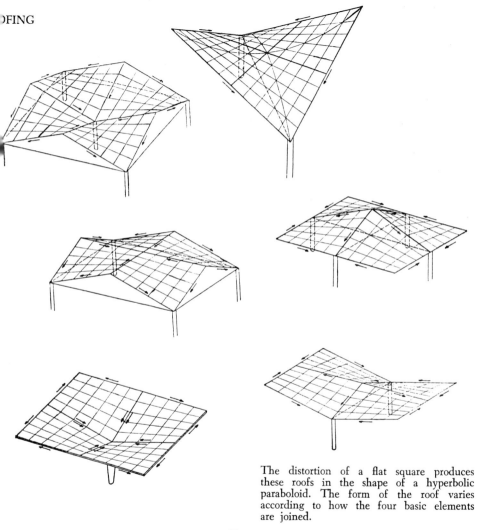

The distortion of a flat square produces these roofs in the shape of a hyperbolic paraboloid. The form of the roof varies according to how the four basic elements are joined.

23

PEANO'S CURVE

One of the cardinal principles of geometry is that a point has no dimensions and that a curve has one only and therefore can never fill an area. This is another firm conviction that has been badly shaken—by the " curve of Peano ", which belongs to the supreme type of pathological curves and does fill up an area. It can occupy not only the entire inside of a square but also climb into the space of a complete cubic box. The successive stages of this curve may be seen in the following figures:

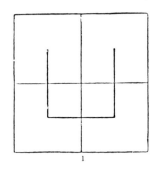

1

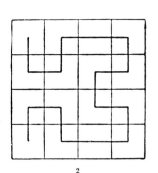

2

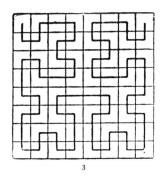

3

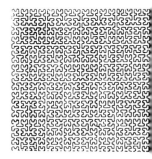

Take any point in a square or cube. It can be demonstrated that the curve, when completed, will pass through this point. And since the same reasoning may be applied to any other point, the logical conclusion is that the curve must fill the whole of the square or cube. Mathematicians once held that every curve must, of necessity, have tangents, because, they said, this property is axiomatic. But now, in 1890, Peano, to their great amazement, had devised a curve that would not admit tangents at any point, a curve that filled the entire area of a square, and for that reason could only be re-

presented by a square black patch. Since then curves without tangents have become familiar to mathematicians.

CHECKERS

Checker players in the open air at Bournemouth.

ISLAMIC DECORATION

Islamic mural decoration of the thirteenth century.

DIAGONAL

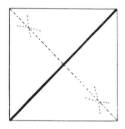

Given the diagonal, construct the square.

DIAGONALS

The diagonals of these two figures are equal.

DIATOM

Microscopic algae are of various form including the square.

26

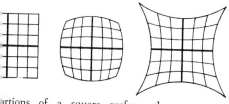

rtions of a square surface, the two
ans remaining constant.

DOUBLING

The problem of doubling the square was easily solved by the Greeks, by constructing a second square on the diagonal of the first. But this raised another problem: the doubling of the cube. Working on this problem Menelaus of Alexandria tried in vain to solve it with a construction of straight lines and arcs of circles and with other curves. After much work, instead of getting the double of the cube, he discovered the ellipse, parabola and hyperbola.

ALBRECHT DÜRER

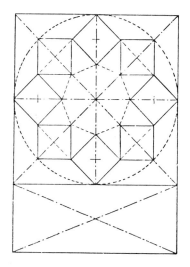

Proportions of the church of Santa Maria degli Angeli, Rome, after Dürer.

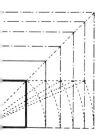

n a square, describe its double, triple, uple, quintuple, etc.

INTERNAL DIVISIONS

Division of a square into two rectangles at points determined by various combinations of arcs and lines derived from the dimensions of the square itself.

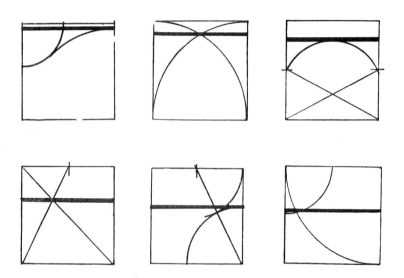

THE DUOMO OF PISA

Proportions of the façade of the Duom of Pisa.

GOD OF THE TEMPEST

The Temple of the God of the Tempest at Carchemish. The sanctuary of the temple was a perfect square.

VAN DOESBURG

Arithmetical composition, 1930.

HEXAGON

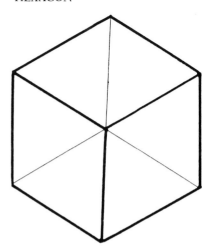

The projection of a cube with two opposite corners in line is a hexagon.

IVORY LABELS

Ivory labels with numerical markings, found in the royal tomb attributed to Menes founder of the first dynasty, at Nagada in Egypt.

square circumscribing a given circle
twice the area of the square inscribed
he same circle.

The Empty Box, painting, 1954.

ARE HANDKERCHIEF

ene from Verdi's *Othello*.

IRON

In a mass of molten iron, the transformation from liquid to solid, on cooling, comes about by the formation of crystalloid nuclei in the form of cubes (as may be seen in a series of microphotographs) which multiply rapidly along crystallographic axes until the whole mass is filled.

TRENCH

Character used in writings of the Bamum (a tribe of the Cameroons) to indicate "trench". Similar characters are also to be found in ancient Sinaitic writings.

FORMS DERIVED FROM THE SQUARE

Two-dimensional compositions derived from combining, rotating or modifying square surfaces.

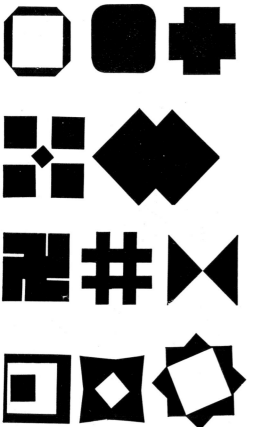

FLUORITE

Rectangular structure of fluorite crystal

WINDMILL

Four cuts along the diagonals of a square of cardboard make this simple toy.

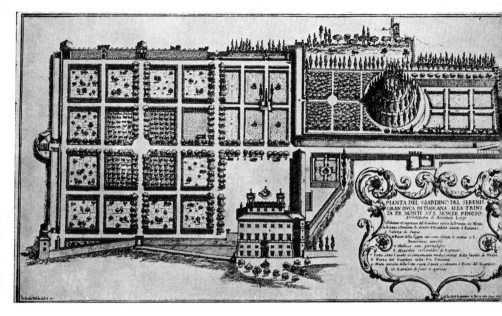

The gardens of the Villa Medici, on the
Pincio, in Rome. Architect: Annibale Lippi.

SUNFLOWER

The arrangement of the seeds of the
flower follows the logarithmic spiral.

GAMES

Chess, checkers, dominoes, puss in the corner, are among the games derived from the square.

THE 15 PUZZLE

The 15 Puzzle, as its inventor Sam Lloyd called it in 1878, was a great success. Employers had to put up notices forbidding their employees to play the game during working hours, under pain of dismissal. A French journalist of the time described it as more harmful than tobacco or alcohol, responsaible for migraine, neuralgia and neuroses.

Enormous prizes were offered for the solution of apparently simple problems, but nobody ever won them. The 15 numbers and the one empty space may theoretically be arranged in the box in 20,922,-789,888,000 different ways.

But two American mathematicians, Johnson and Story, proved that, starting from any given position, and pushing the numbers around in the box, only half of the total number of possible positions may be reach-

ed. This meant that if there were [t]trillion positions that could be reached, the[y] were ten trillion more that could not. And the fact that half the starting positio[ns] in the puzzle were incapable of soluti[on] explains why the generous prizes we[re] never won, for it always happened t[hat] the prize contests involved one of th[e] impossible positions.

GRADATIONS IN TEXTURE

Gradations in texture obtained by distort[ing] the squares in a chequered pattern. Ulm School, 1957.

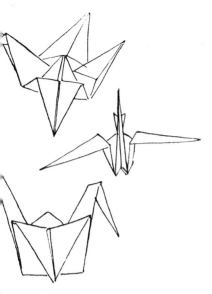

make public the theory of incommensurables, perished in a shipwreck because, according to the legend, the inexpressible and the unimaginable should have remained hidden for all time. So the man, whose crime was that he had unwittingly revealed one of the secrets of nature, was sent back to his place of origin to remain lashed by the waves for ever.

It is probable that the legend grew out of a very real resentment against the revealing of results, particularly to outsiders, which were certainly very embarrassing in that they demonstrated the error of the Pythagorean conception of the point. After this discovery, in fact, a revision of the fundamental concepts of geometry began take place, leading to the celebrated sophsophisms of Zeno, and eventually to the Elements of Euclid.

GOTHIC

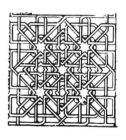

Ornamental Gothic motifs.

·ANESE TOYS

merous toys can be made by the Japae game of folding a square of paper in ous ways. Famous examples are a bird ch moves its wings, a foldable box, an ·ct in the shape of four hollow pyra-·ls, upside down and joined together, in-·which one can put four fingers.

COMMENSURABLES

·withstanding the Pythagorean concep-·, of the extended point, incommensura-·, i.e. quantities that have no common ·sure, exist. It seems that the discovery ·he incommensurability between the side · the diagonal of the square was made ·Hippasus of Metapontum, a disciple of ·hagoras, who, having been the first to

HOMO QUADRATUS

In the theory of Homo Quadratus, num
first principle of the universe, acquires s
bolic significance, founded on a series
numerical correspondences which are
aesthetic correspondences. The earliest fo
of the theory related to music. The m
cal tones are eight, observed an unkn
Carthusian monk, because four were
covered by the ancients and four were
ed by the moderns (he was referring
the four authentic modes and the
plagal modes). For other writers, and
popular belief, the number four was a
number of great efficacy, a fertile procre
of series. There are four cardinal po
four principal winds, four phases of
moon, four seasons; four is the constitu
number of Timaeus' tetrahedral corpu
of fire, and there are four letters in
name ADAM. And four, too, as Vitru
teaches, is the number of man, since
width of a man with his arms outstret
corresponds to his height, thus forming
base and height of an ideal square;
four is the number of moral perfec
for the man who is morally fortified st
four-square against attack.

MAX HUBER

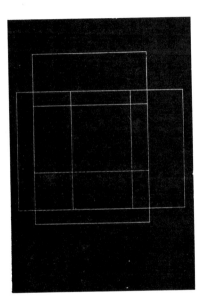

Composition on a square basis.

PHOTOGRAPHIC COMPOSITION
by Max Huber

OPTICAL ILLUSIONS

Optical illusions of Hering (or Helmholtz) on square areas.

ROMANESQUE INITIALS

From a twelfth-century manuscript.

CUBIC LAMP

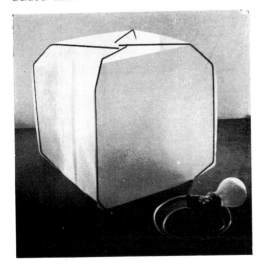

The shape of this lamp, contained within a cube, allows easy assembly and dismantling by means of the two diagonal metal supports. The simple design makes it very inexpensive to produce.

KARL GERSTNER

Blue-yellow sequence on red, 1958-59.

"The infinite is a square—without corners."
Ancient Chinese saying.

THE CHINESE AND PYTHAGORAS

About five centuries before Pythagoras, the
Chinese knew about the relation between
the sides of a right-angled triangle. The
proof, found in the "Book of King Chu-Pei-
Yuan", does not actually demonstrate the
theorem of Pythagoras, but one closely al-
lied to it.

Let a and b be the two sides of a right-
angled triangle (the sides about the right
angle). Place one after the other in a
straight line. With this line as base, construct the square ABCD. Mark the point of
contact of the two segments a and b on all
four sides of the square, at E, F, G and H,
as shown in the figure. Join EF and GH so
that the square ABCD is now divided into
an area that is the square of a, an area
that is the square of b, and two rectangles
each of area ab. Divide each of these two
rectangles diagonally, and we have four
equal right-angled triangles with hypote-
nuse c.

Place the four right-angled triangles on the
area ABCD so that the right angles of the
triangles coincide with the right angles of
the square, and we obtain an area in the
middle of which is the square on the hypo-
tenuse c.

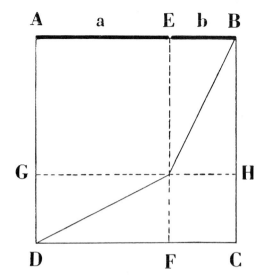

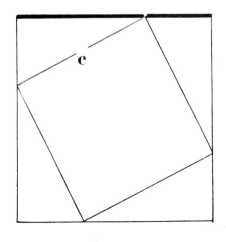

KLEE

LE CORBUSIER

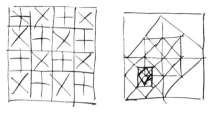

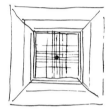

Studies in squares by Klee.

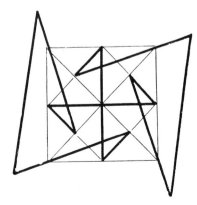

Dynamic exfoliation of a given static.

Museum of unlimited extendability, se from above. Built on piles with entran from the central court. Infinite possibilit of internal arrangement with prefabricat units.

MAZES

Plans of mazes in Italian villa gardens the seventeenth century.

42

LEONARDO

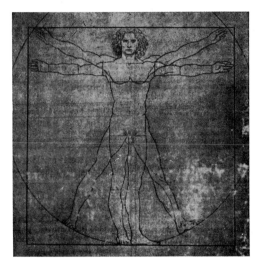

Study of the proportions of the human figure, enclosed in a square.

Those adept in Egyptian priesthood considered the square as the expression of man, in that man, in an upright position with arms outstretched was found to be of equal measure in height and width.

LEONARDO

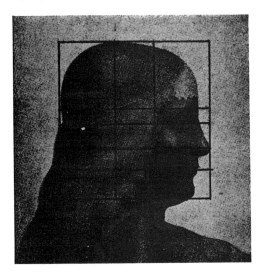

Proportions of a profile.

GREEK FRET

VERENA LOEWENSBERG

Composition 257, 1956-57.

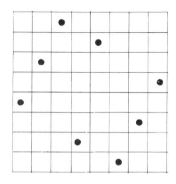

blem: place eight queens on an ordi-
y chessboard of sixty-four squares in
a way that none is in check from any
he others. It was proposed by Nauck in
0 and solved by him, and by various
rs later. Ninety-two solutions are possi-
Here are two of them, the second of
ch is symmetrical, i.e. it remains un-
nged if the board is turned through
degrees.

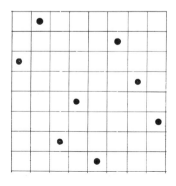

RICHARD P. LOHSE

Horizontal divisions, 1949-53.

KAZIMIR MALEVICH

" When in 1913, in my desperate attempt
to liberate art from the useless burden of
the object, I sought refuge in the form of
the square, and exhibited a picture that
represented nothing but a black square on
a white ground, the critics did not like it;
nor did the public: ' All that we loved has
been lost, we are now in the desert. Before
us there is nothing but a black square on
a white ground '. The perfect square seemed to both critics and public something
incomprehensible and menacing—which is
what one might have expected.

The ascent to the summit of non-figurative
art is a difficult and agonizing climb, but
satisfying nevertheless. At every step real
things recede more and more into the dis-
tance, objects become merged into each
other, until finally the world of ordinary
ideas, in which, however, we live, fades out
altogether. Away with the images of reality,
away with ideal representations—nothing but
the desert!

But this desert is full of the spirit of non-
objective sensibility, which penetrates every-
where.

I, too, had a kind of timidity, and I hesi-
tated to the point of anguish when I was
about to abandon the ' world of will and
representation ', in which I had lived and
created, believing in its authenticity.

But the feeling of satisfaction which came
with my liberation from the object took me
still further into the desert, up to the point
where nothing was authentic except sensibility—and so sensibility became the very
substance of my life.

The picture that I had exhibited was not an
empty picture, but sensibility in the ab-
sence of the object.

Painting is overtaken by time, and the paint-
er is a prejudice of the past. "

Suprematist composition, painting 1915?

ent to the Resistance, at Udine.
by the architects Valle and Marco-
from above.

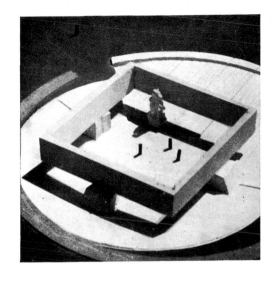

MARI

tic experimental research with cubic

CHINESE COINS

Chinese coins with square holes.

USELESS MACHINE

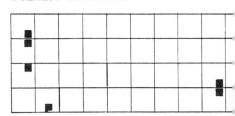

Harmonic sketch of the six elements w
compose Munari's "Useless Machine 19
The six elements (strips of natural
dized aluminium of various lengths) p
together on one level occupy the spac
two and a half squares. Suspended
threads of nylon they can be arrange
infinite combinations.

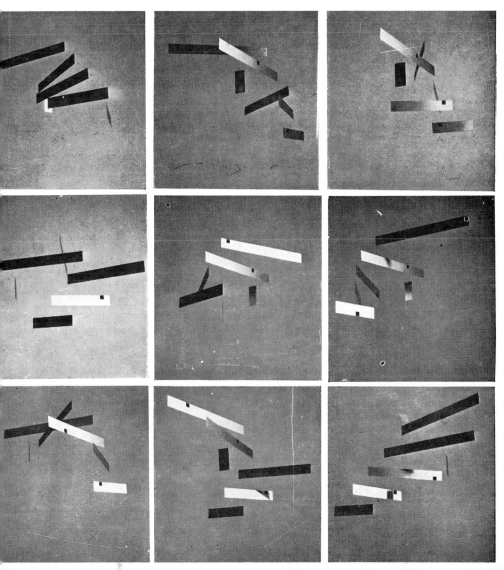

MODULOR

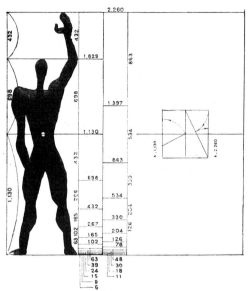

Le Corbusier's modulor is a unit of measurement based on the human figure and on mathematics.

MONDRIAN

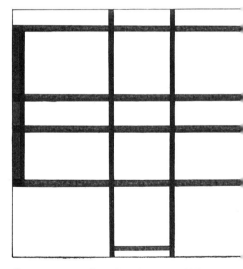

Composition with red, painting, 1936.

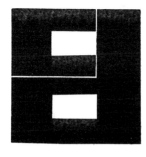

HALF

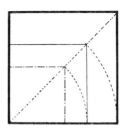

Given a square, describe one of half, and one of a quarter of its area.

NICAEA

The town of Nicaea in Bithynia (about 300 B.C.) was in the form of a square of about 700 meters a side, with two main streets which crossed at right angles and joined the four gates of the town.

MUSICAL NOTES

A line of music written in the eleventh century.

SPIRAL NEBULA

The logarithmic spiral is also found in the form of some nebulae.

PIER LUIGI and ANTONIO NERVI

The winning model in the competition for

the "Palace of Work" at Turin. construction by Pier Luigi and Ant Nervi involves a roof of sixteen inde dent square structures of 40 meters a with a pillar for every 1,600 square m of roof.

NEGATIVE POSITIVE

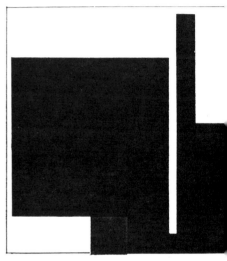

Pictorial composition without backgro in white, black and red. Munari, 1951.

NINTH ORDER

Magic square of the ninth order comp according to Bachet's rule.
The sum of the numbers in each ver column or in each horizontal row is ways the same.

28	69	20	61	12	53	4	45
68	19	60	11	52	3	44	76
27	59	10	51	2	43	75	35
58	18	50	1	42	74	34	66
17	49	9	41	73	33	65	25
48	8	40	81	32	64	24	56
7	39	80	31	72	23	55	15
38	79	30	71	22	63	14	46
78	29	70	21	62	13	54	5

NOTRE-DAME

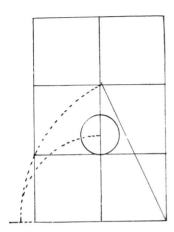

Scheme of the façade of Notre-Dame.

OPERA QUADRATA

An ancient system of masonry, found in Etruria and Latium, in which square blocks of marble or tufa were used.

COUNTRY

Japanese ideogram for " country ": an enclosure (the frontiers) contains a mouth (the people) and a bow (the army).

PAVILION

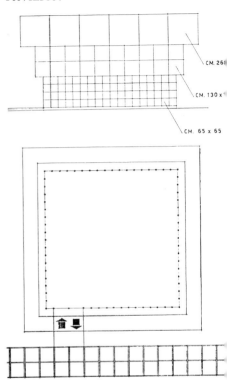

CM. 260

CM. 130 x

CM. 65 x 65

Textile Pavilion at the Eleventh Trien Exhibition at Milan, by the architect Ed do Sianesi. Plan and one of the four eq sides.

SQUARE PYRAMID

A square of cardboard with many alternat cuts, as shown in the illustration, suspen at the center, automatically forms this th dimensional figure.

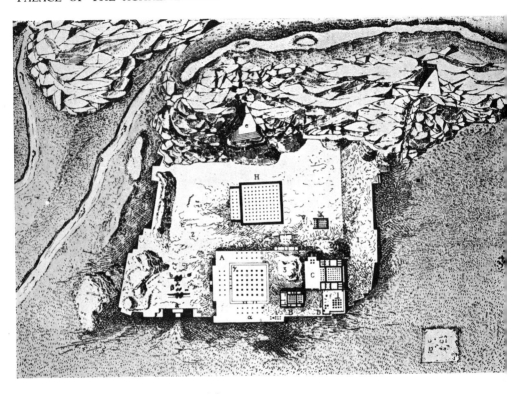

General plan of the Palace of the Achae-
menidae at Persepolis (reconstruction).

PALLADIO

The use of the square in the architecture of Palladio is often the vital element in his buildings. The Villa Foscarini, near Stra, has a square ground-plan. Other square ar-chitectural areas are to be found in Villa Thiene at Quinto Vicentino, in Palazzo Iseppo de' Porti and in the Pa Thiene, both at Vicenza.

56

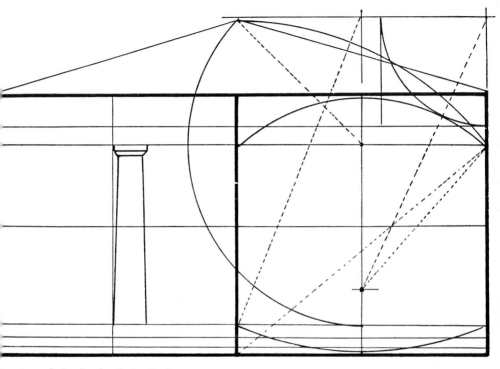

portions of the façade of the Parthenon.

PLATO

" We have divided the whole series of numbers into two classes: every number that
can be formed by multiplying two equal
factors we have represented in a figure
with a square and we have called it a
square and equilateral number. "

PALAZZO FARNESE

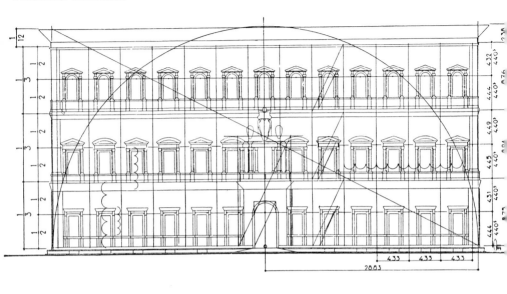

白い四角   JAPANESE POEM

のなか

の白い四角   white square of
       inside the

のなか   white square of
       inside the

の白い四角   white square of
       inside the

のなか   white square of

の白い四角   inside the

のなか   white square

の白い四角   Katué Kitasono

ho is born square will not die round.
apolitan proverb.

RSE

The form of the cube in nature: cubic iron pyrites from Elba.

ther purse. It is closed by folding along diagonals of the vertical walls of the cube.

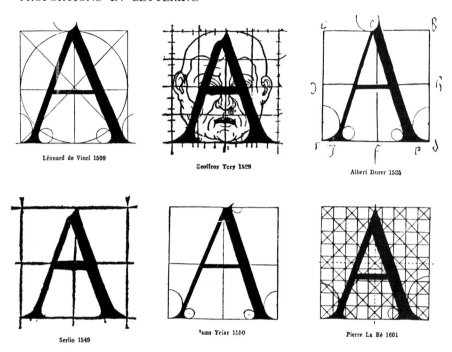

Léonard de Vinci 1509

Geoffroy Tory 1529

Albert Durer 1525

Serlio 1549

Juan Yciar 1550

Pierre La Bé 1601

Studies in proportions for the letters of the alphabet: Leonardo 1509, Geoffroy Tory 1529, Albrecht Dürer 1525, Serlio, 1549, Juan Yciar 1550, Pierre La Bé 1601.

SQUARE - WINDOW

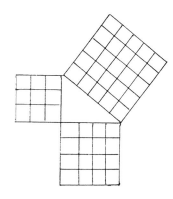

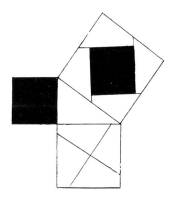

illustrations of the Pythagorian theo-

" A woman suffering from a brain disease, was incapable of copying a square, and it was evident that the figure meant nothing to her. On being asked what it was, she replied that it was something to do with a window. After many tests it became evident that she was only able to copy those models which to her looked like concrete objects. When she saw that she could not copy a model, because it had no meaning for her, she would sometimes modify it in such a way that it took on the characteristics of a concrete object; after which she was able to copy it.

Given a square, she produced the following:

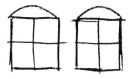

When asked what these figures might mean, she replied, ' The windows of a church '. She did not draw squares without significance, but two windows of a church in a position in which one could really find them. Evidently where we see an abstract geometric figure the patient could only see a concrete object. "

MAGIC SQUARES

A magic square of the *n*th order is a square divided, like a chessboard, into n^2 smaller squares, or cells, where *n* is the number of cells in any side. Numbers are then inserted in the cells in such a way that the sum of the numbers in any line, horizontal or vertical, or in either of the two diagonals, is always the same. This sum is called the magic constant.

A magic square remains unaffected when subjected to any of the following changes, termed simple transformations:

a - rotation about the center through one, two or three right angles, clockwise or counterclockwise;

b - symmetrical reversal about the horizontal or vertical medians;

c - symmetrical reversal about either diagonal;

d - the substitution of every number with its complement in respect of $n^2 + 1$.

Eight magic squares of the third order:

4	3	8		6	7	2
9	5	1		1	5	9
2	7	6		8	3	4

3	9	4		8	1	6
7	5	3		3	5	7
6	1	8		4	9	2

2	7	6		4	9	2
9	5	1		3	5	7
4	3	8		8	1	6

8	3	4		6	1	8
1	5	9		7	5	3
6	7	2		2	9	4

Magic squares, which the old Indian mathematicians already knew how to construct, first became known in Europe in about 1420. In the Middle Ages they were believed to have supernatural powers and were worn as amulets against the evil eye, plague and other diseases. They had special meanings for astrologers: for Cornelius Agrippa the magic square of the first order symbolized unity and eternity; the impossibility of a magic square of the second order indicated the imperfection of the four elements (air, water, earth and fire); the seven magic squares of the third to the ninth orders represented the seven planets then known.

16	3	2	13
5	10	11	8
9	6	7	12
4	15	14	1

e following magic square of the fourth
er is to be found in one of Albert Dü-
s grotesques called "Melancholy", 1514,
ich year figures in the center of the
tom row.

go Palomino published a work on magic
ares in Madrid, in 1599, without, how-
r, giving any procedure for their construc-
. In 1612, C. G. Bachet published a
hod for constructing those of odd-num-
ed orders. De la Loubère published an-
r method in 1691, called the border me-
d. In 1693, P. H. De la Hire published
method for constructing squares of even-
nbered orders, due to B. Frénicle, and
e all the 880 possible solutions for a
gic square of the fourth order.

ABOLIC SQUARES

er then constructed "panmagic" squares
which the sum of the numbers situ-
d in every pair of complementary lines
aning by that any pair of diagonal lines,
on either side of and parallel to the
ral diagonal, whose total numbers of
s is n), is also equal to the magic con-
t. The following square of the fourth
er, for example. is panmagic:

1	12	7	14
8	13	2	11
10	3	16	5
15	6	9	4

Several studies on diabolic squares, as they
were called by E. Lucas, A. H. Frost,
M. Frolow and others, appeared between
1866 and 1886. Diabolic squares have the
property of remaining magic when they are
divided into two rectangles by any line
parallel to the sides, the positions of which
are then exchanged. The following is a
diabolic square of the fourth order:

1	14	4	15
12	7	9	6
13	2	16	3
8	11	5	10

In 1849, E. Maillet published his researches
on a general theory of magic squares based
on the general theory of the substitution of
n letters. G. Arnoux published "Les espaces
arithmétiques hypermagiques" in Paris in
1894, where he evolved a very remark-
able method for the construction of magic
squares of the fourth order, a method later
extended by A. Margossian in 1908 to the
case of magic squares of any composite order.

SATANIC SQUARES

Interesting researches have, moreover, been
published by A. Aubry in 1926 in "Sphinx-
Oedipe". A magic square is termed bi-
magic if its numbers can be substituted by
their squares; trimagic if they can also be
substituted by their cubes. Such squares
are also called satanic or cabbalistic.

MILITARY SQUARE

Ranks of soldiers drawn up in square formation.

MILITARY QUADRILATERAL

A quadrangular area of ground defended by four forts.

SQUARING THE CIRCLE

The most famous problem in the history of mathematics is the squaring of the circle. The first elements of geometry dealt with the possibilities of measuring a figure restricted to straight lines. In the Nile valley, where every year the floods obliterated any marks made by the farmers to indicate the bounds of their property, geometry helped to redefine them. Areas bounded by curved lines made difficulties in the calculations and it was sought to simplify the problem by defining the areas with straight lines only. If a square which had the same area as a circle could be constructed, by measuring the area of the square, one would also have that of the circle. The expression " squaring the circle " has its origin in this fact, but the difficulty of doing so was due to the nature of π.

SQUARE - TRIANGLE

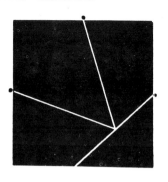

A square, cut as shown and hinged at points indicated, is transformed into equilateral triangle by swinging the paround on the level to their new position

FOUR POINTS IN SPACE

The four corner points are enough to g the impression of a square.

ANCIENT ROME

According to an ancient tradition, mentioned by some Greek authors, it seems that there was probably a Roma Quadrata distinct from that founded by Romulus, and older. From various historical sources and archeological discoveries, it appears that this Roma quadrata must have consisted of a square cell on the Palatine Hill in front of the Temple of Apollo, in which were preserved, before the city was founded, all the objects of good omen for its foundation, and which was closed with a square stone.

Hence the tradition of a Roma Quadrata older than that of Romulus: what was originally nothing a but a small cell gave its name to the whole new city, which was called Roma Quadrata or Roma Romulea indifferently.

ROTATION

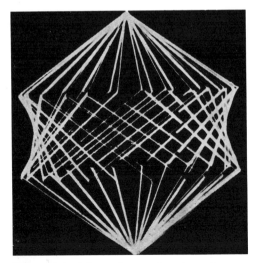

Figure derived from the rotation of a cube.

RENAISSANCE

Painted decoration.

RAMSES IV

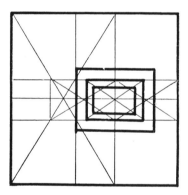

Proportional analysis of the plan of tomb of Ramses IV.

RING

PROPORTIONAL RECTANGLES

Lowering the diagonal of a square onto the prolongation of the base, we get a rectangle in which, whatever the unit of measurement, the ratio between the sides is $1 : \sqrt{2}$. Continuing the process we get a series of rectangles with the following ratios: $1 : \sqrt{3}$, $1 : \sqrt{4}$ (i.e. an area of two squares, $1 : \sqrt{5}$, and so on.

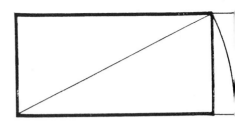

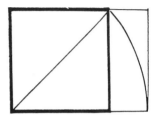

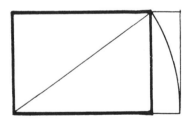

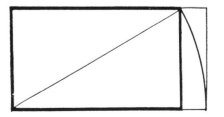

CHESS IN MOSCOW

The opening of the Twelfth World Ch Championship in the Central Theatre the Soviet Army in Moscow.

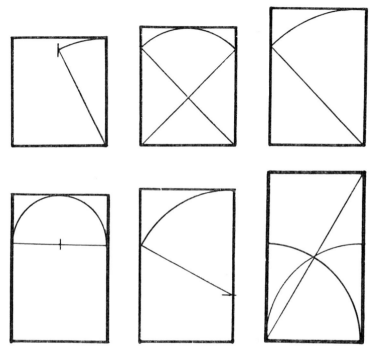

Rectangles obtained by the elongation of a square to various extents determined by certain of its own inherent measurements.

*Raphael. *The Marriage of the Virgin.*

SDOM

ancients represented Fortune seated on ound stone and Wisdom seated on a re stone, thereby showing that the er is fickle while the seat of the lat- is firm and immovable.

PREHISTORIC SIGNS

Signs painted in blue-black and linear-red, of the most ancient series, found at Cachao da Rapa or Curral das Letras, Braganca. Similar signs are to be found also in paleo-Babylonian, northern Semitic and American proto-Indian writings.

THE KNIGHT'S TOUR

The problem of moving the knight through all sixty-four squares of the chessboard in sixty-three moves, known to the ancient Indian mathematicians, has a number of solutions not yet determined.
Euler and various other mathematicians indicated ways of solving the problem. Here are two solutions (the numbers denote the successive positions of the knight) of which

43	40	15	26	13	30	5	8
38	25	42	29	16	7	12	31
41	44	39	14	27	4	9	6
24	37	28	17	54	11	32	3
45	18	23	64	33	2	55	10
36	49	46	19	22	53	58	61
47	20	51	34	63	60	1	56
50	35	48	21	52	57	62	59

the second is " closed ", that is from the final position the knight can, in one move, return to his initial position:

BRUNO SERVI

The square represents number at its highest perfection, because, in its case, the number of times the base is repeated is also the number of times unity is repeated in the base.
In squaring, in fact, the mere enunciation of the base expresses in itself the number of times it is repeated; so that every external or arbitrary element is eliminated which, in the determination of the number of times of repetition, is always present in any other nonpotential operation.

ROCK-SALT

The square in nature: a crystal of rock salt.

22	25	50	39	52	35	60	57
27	40	23	36	49	58	53	34
24	21	26	51	38	61	56	59
41	28	37	48	3	54	33	62
20	47	42	13	32	63	4	55
29	16	19	46	43	2	7	10
18	45	14	31	12	9	64	5
15	30	17	44	1	6	11	8

TRAFFIC SIGNS

Right of precedence; right of precedence ends.

GOLDEN SECTION

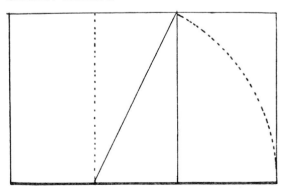

Method of determining the golden section,

LIBYAN CHARACTERS

Characters of Libyan writing.

SQUARE WRITING

Almost every country has a so-called square form for the letters of its alphabet or its ideograms. In Rome, the ancient capital letters used for monumental inscriptions were called " square ". Hebrew, Chinese and Japanese writing is square. Obviously a square form allows the best composition on a flat surface of vertical or horizontal texts.

Characters of Balti writing, of the state of Kashmir, corresponding to the respective phonetic values: d, ts, b, h, k. Many characters of this writing, which is presumed to have been invented at the time of the conversion of the people to Islam around 1400, seem to have had, as their original basis, a square grid.
Such a grid probably gave an easily remembered form to each letter.

instructions for the figures of square dances according to Carson Robison. Formation: ur couples in one group. Form a square ith a couple face to face on every side. group should occupy a square space of ne feet per side. Every lady is on the ght of her partner. The lady on the left every gentleman is the corner lady. The incipal couple, that is couple number ie, dances back toward the part of the ll where the orchestra is. The couple on e right of the principal couple is couple imber two, and so on for the third and urth, or last couple.

onor: the gentlemen bow, the ladies ds.

ving: the gentleman takes the right hand the lady on his left and puts his arm ound her waist, as for a waltz. He places his right foot on the outside of the right foot of the lady and they dance around in a clockwise direction, spinning on the right foot.

Promenade: the couples cross hands and circle around the group in an counterclockwise direction.

Do-si-do: the lady and gentleman move towards each other and pass, right shoulder to right shoulder. Each takes a step to the right, passing back to back, and then both return to their original positions.

Allemande left: each gentleman faces towards his corner lady. They take each other by the left hand and wheel clockwise returning to their original positions. Grand right and left: the partners face each other and take each other by the right hand. They move towards each other and pass. The gentlemen spin counterclockwise and the ladies clockwise. Take the left hand of your neighbour, pass, and in this way proceed in a circle. Some titles of square dances: The Square Waltz, Square Dance Polka, Promenade Indian Style, Around the Outside, Birdie in the Cage.

RUNIC CHARACTERS

From a Runic alphabet, phonetic value: Oe, ae, e, o. The square has the phonetic value: ng.

THE LOGARITHMIC SPIRAL

From a square we can obtain a golden rectangle by lowering the diagonal between the center of the base and an opposite corner onto the prolongation of the base. If, to this rectangle, we attach another square based on the longer side we obtain another golden rectangle. Continuing attaching squares to the longer sides of the rectangles we obtain a figure composed of squares making a spiral form around the pole O, which is the point of intersection of the diagonals of the successive rectangles. If we draw a curve through the points of intersection of these diagonals with the successive squares, the curve will be a logarithmic spiral.

This curve represents the law of visible organic growth, especially in shells, in the arrangement of sunflower seeds, in some spiral nebulae and in many other cases.

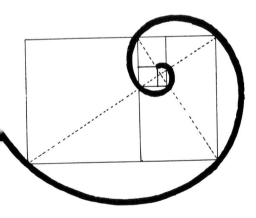

LOCKS

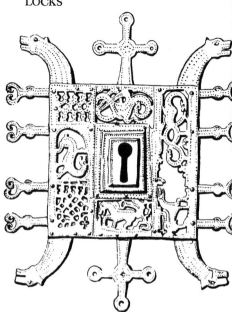

Twelfth-century Scandinavian lock.

TATAMI

A tatami is a piece of thick matting wit which the Japanese have been covering th floors of their houses for more than thousand years. The tatami is two squar in size and serves as a basic unit of me surement in the building plan of a hous Every room is conceived on the basis the number of tatami to be used, and it sufficient to just state the number of t tami to be used in a room to get an id of its shape and dimensions, and as eve part of the house is based on the tata formula, one may plan without having make measurements.

FOSSIL SPONGE

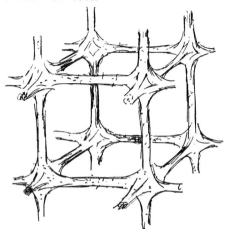

Structure of a fossil sponge.

HITTITE CHARACTERS

Hittite characters. Part of a hieroglyph from inscriptions found at Hama, in Syria. The second character has the phonetic value: k, g.

SEAL

Sign from a proto-Indian seal.

EMPIRE STYLE

Detail of an Empire style balustrade.

ANTON STANKOWSKI

Poster design.

A square cut in this way may be recomposed in many other ways.

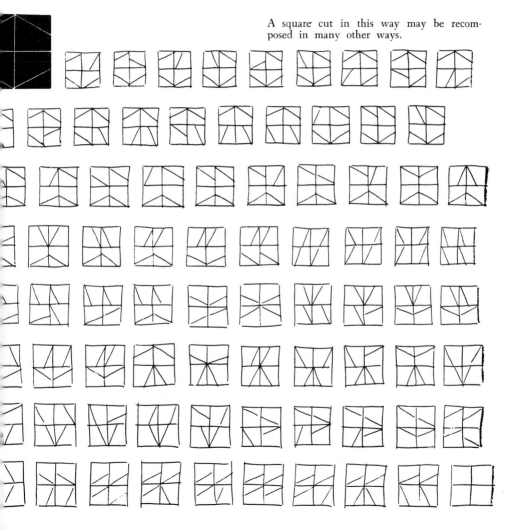

TETRAHEDRON

A tetrahedron may be cut into two identical pieces, the area of section being a square.

TELL EL AMARNA

A model village at Tell el Amarna (1370 B.C.) in which lived the workers and artisans employed on the construction of the tombs in the rock in the higher part of the desert. This village, situated in a desolate valley, far from water but near the cliffs where the tombs were to be cut out of the rock, was square in shape and surrounded by a high wall in which there was only one entrance. In the village itself there were five narrow streets which ran parallel from north to south, through lines of small, rentable houses, all identical in shape. Only in the south-east corner, near the gate, was there a bigger and more elaborate building, which was probably the house of the supervisor.

The monotony of all these houses was compensated for by the variety of what they contained. The men who worked in the tombs as painters and decorators used to bring home some of the colors, with the result that the walls of their houses were all decorated with rough designs. During the excavations, tools of every kind were found: clay crucibles, unworked precious stones, parts of looms, and rings with unfinished cut stones.

The well-protected houses in the city itself, of members of the court, seemed inhuman and without life in comparison with this humble workers' village.

TRIGON

A Swiss game composed of squares cut-up in such a way that different figures may be formed.

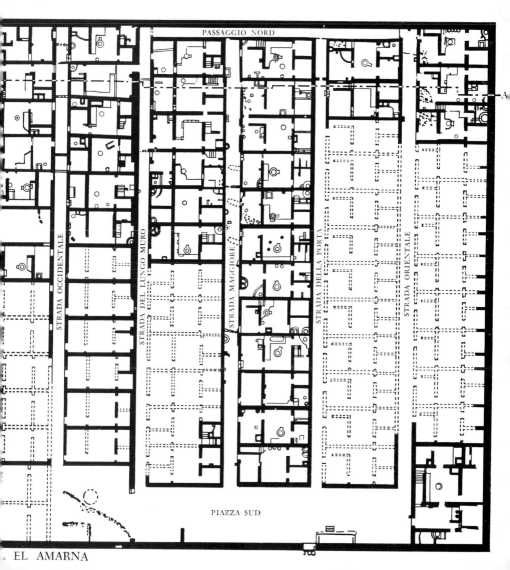

PASSAGGIO NORD

STRADA OCCIDENTALE

STRADA DEL LUNGO MURO

STRADA MAGGIORE

STRADA DELLA PORTA

STRADA ORIENTALE

A

PIAZZA SUD

EL AMARNA

THE TEMPLE OF SOLOMON

The Temple of Solomon in Jerusalem. The Holy of Holies was a perfect square, with sides almost equal to that of Carchemish. It was completely bare, except for the front which was adorned with a curtain embroidered in various colors.

ONE QUARTER GREATER

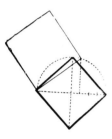

Given a square, describe another one greater by a quarter.

A FIFTH

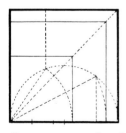

Given a square, describe another one fifth, two thirds, etc., smaller.

TETRAFLEX

Three-dimensional construction made wi four squares fixed together at their paral sides and having a cordon for every d gonal. This object may be folded in ma ways always following the lines of t folds.

TWIDDLE

Cubic object cut in sixteen equal prisma parts. These parts are hinged to each oth in such a way as to allow its transform tion into other parallelepipedal or prisn tic objects, always keeping all the pie attached to each other.

PHYSIOGNOMIC TYPES OF LEDOS

The square type indicates an energe blunt nature, a firmness of character the point of inflexibility, that may eas degenerate into stubbornness. An able r soner, strictly and powerfully logical, wi a well developed practical sense; having propensity for the exact sciences, for p losophy and mathematics, but lacking imagination, which allows little aptitu for the arts. A lover of construction, has the mental attitude of the archite His nature, sceptical and doubting, lea him to materialism; if faith illuminates soul it will rest on unshakeable foundatio the head will always control the heart. This type generally lives long.

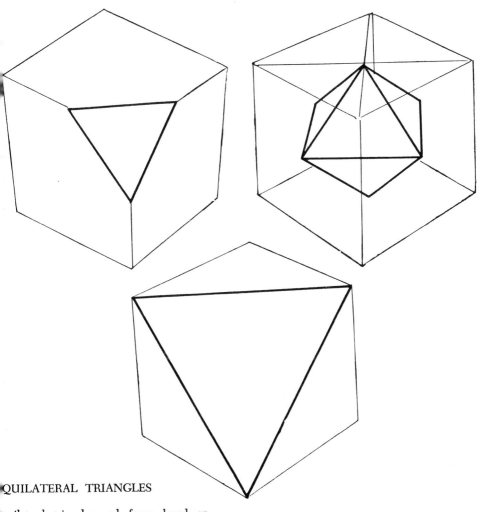

QUILATERAL TRIANGLES

quilateral triangles and forms based on
uilateral triangles in cubic spaces.

UO

Mayan character; phonetic value: uo.

$1 \times 5 - 2 \times 2.$

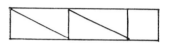

Apparent transformation of a rectangle 1×5 into a square 2×2.

URANIUM AND GRAPHITE

A large cube of uranium and graphite for the first nuclear reactor.

VASARELY

Detail of a large composition in black and white.

82

MIES VAN DER ROHE

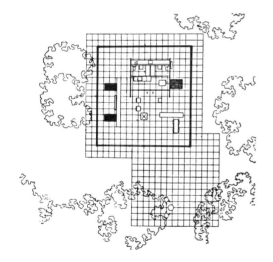

Plan and front elevation of the " 50 × 50 "

MARY VIEIRA

From square to cube. Form in stainle
steel 35 × 35 × 35 cm. Basle, 1959. C
lection of Dr. Markus Kutter, Basle.

WANG HSI-CHIH

Wang Hsi-Chih, who lived in the time
the Eastern Chin dynasty (A.D. 316-420),
considered the true father of Chinese ca
graphy. He perfected the " li ssu " chara
ters by giving them their beautiful squa
form, as well as the script which nowada
we call cursive, still undeveloped in h
time, and he invented an intermediary for
between the two. The present-day Chine
characters therefore belong to one or other
the three forms he established: square
medium and cursive. To him is due th
merit for having perfected them in such
highly artistic and admirable manner.

一面一面的比較話句子跟圖,就明白話句子的意思了。不用太使勁記,只要留心話句子怎麼變意思怎麼跟着變就成了。這麼樣學英國話,不大像用功,倒很像遊戲。

用這本書的時候,越把中國話忘掉越好,圖就會把意思告訴你了。在這會兒把英國話翻成中國話,只有學起來更困難的。有一套留聲機片把書上的話說給你聽,說一句歇一歇,為是你好跟着說。如果你自己用功,沒有這套留聲機片,頂好先學認字用字,等有了幫手再學念學說。每次兩三面一塊兒練習直到背得出圖上的話句子為止。造句子的時候別淨靠死記;想法兒用英國話體

INDEX

As all the subjects in this book have been arranged in alphabetical order (as far as make-up allows) no index is necessary.

English translation by Desmond O' Grady.

ibliography:

Maurice Kraitchik   LA MATHÈMATIQUE DES JEUX
BAUHAUS   The Museum of Modern Art, New York.
Marcel Poëte   LA CITTÀ ANTICA
Diringer   L'ALFABETO NELLA STORIA DELLA CIVILTÀ
Drexler   THE ARCHITECTURE OF JAPAN   The Museum of Modern Art, New York.
Ernst Mössel   VOM GEHEIMNIS DER FORM UND DER URFORM DES SEINS, Stuttgart
Gyorgy Kepes   LANGUAGE OF VISION   Theobald, Chicago.
Gyorgy Kepes   THE NEW LANDSCAPE   Theobald, Chicago.
Karl Gerstner   KALTE KUNST? Niggli, Teufen AR,
Wolfgang von Wersin   DAS BUCH VOM RECHTECK   Maier, Ravensburg.
Steinhaus   MATHEMATICAL SNAPSHOTS   Oxford University Press, New York.
David Katz   LA PSICOLOGIA DELLA FORMA
G. Ronchetti   DIZIONARIO ILLUSTRATO DEI SIMBOLI
Karnes and Newman   MATEMATICA E IMMAGINAZIONE
ENCICLOPEDIA DELLE MATEMATICHE ELEMENTARI
Pio Emanuelli   IL CIELO E LE SUE MERAVIGLIE
Umberto Forti   GEOMETRIA PIANA
Leonard Wolley   IL MESTIERE DELL'ARCHEOLOGO
DE STIJL   Stedelijk Museum, Amsterdam.
KONKRETE KUNST   Kunsthalle, Basel.
ARTE ASTRATTA E CONCRETA
AUJOURD'HUI, Paris, n. 3-4-9.
CIVILTÀ DELLE MACCHINE,
SCIENTIFIC AMERICAN,   New York, May 1958, November 1958.
ILLUSTRAZIONE SCIENTIFICA,
ART, Paris.
ENCICLOPEDIA DELLA CIVILTÀ ATOMICA,
Boris de Rachewiltz   INCONTRO CON L'ARTE EGIZIANA,
Henry Poincaré   LA SCIENCE ET L'HIPOTHÈSE.
Luigi Dami   I GIARDINI ITALIANI
Hornung's Handbook of   DESIGN and DEVICES   Dover Publication, New York.
Cesare Bairati   LA SIMMETRIA DINAMICA
A. Speltz   LES STYLES DE L'ORNEMENT
Gardner Murphy   SOMMARIO DI PSICOLOGIA
Egmont Colerus   IL ROMANZO DELLA GEOMETRIA
Zevi   POETICA DELL'ARCHITETTURA NEOPLASTICA

Other Books published or distributed by George Wittenborn, Inc.

1018 Madison Avenue, New York, N. Y. 10021
and 91 Montgomery Street, Scarsdale, N. Y. 10583

Aalto (Alvar) Complete Works 1922-1960. over 600 ill. 1963 $18.50

Albers (Josef) Poems and Drawings. 22 ill. rev. ed. 1961 $7.50

Alloway (Lawrence) Ettore Colla, Iron Sculpture. 28 ill. 1960 $8.50

Alvard (Julien and S. Lupasco) Frederic Benrath. 10 ill. 1959 $2.50

American Abstract Artists 1936-1966. Contributions by Albers, Bolotowsky, Kelpe, Lassaw, Mason, Morris, Shaw, Slobodkina and others, ill. 1966 $4.50

American Abstract Artists (Editors) The World of Abstract Art. 162 ill. 1957 $8.50

Annual of Architecture, Structure and Townplanning
>   Vol. 3 Ed. by the Association of Architects, Engineers and Townplanners, India, Honorary editor: Santosh Ghosh. 150 ill. 1963 $9.50
>   Vol. 4 400 ill. 1964 $9.50
>   Vol. 5 in preparation, ready 1967

Architecture: Formes & Fonctions. Ed. by Anthony Krafft
>   Vol. 9 1962-1963 250 p., ill., $9.50
>   Vol. 10 1963-1964 240 p., ill. $10.00
>   Vol. 11 1964-1965. 291 pp., ill. $11.00
>   Vol. 12 1965-1966. 238 pp., ill. $11.00

Art de France, Ed. by Andre Chastel
>   Vol. 1 488 pp., 500 ill. 1960 $17.50

Atchley (Dana) ABC Design. 32 silk-screened p., acetate stencil, limited ed. 1965 $9.00

Atelier 17, Hayter Print Group. 23 ill. 1949 $3.50

Baljeu (Joost) Attempt at a Theory of Synthesist Plastic Expression. 14 ill. 1964 $2.00

Barrett (Douglas) Early Cola Bronzes (850-1014 A.D.) 102 ill., 1965 $13.50

Baumann (Ernst) New Gardens. 500 ill. 1955 $11.50

Beckmann. Max Beckmann, ed. by J. B. Neumann and G. Franke, 48 ill. (Vol. 5 in the Art Lover Library), 1931 $1.50

Berne (Stanley) The Dialogues. 14 surrealist ill. by Matta. limited ed. 1962 $5.00
>   The Multiple Modern Gods and Other Stories. 8 woodcuts by Herman Zaage. 1964 $5.00

Blaser (Werner) Structure and Form in Japan. 205 ill. 1963 $15.00

Bolaffi's Catalogue of Modern Art 1966. 2000 ill. 1966 $40.00

Bosquet (Alain) La Peinture de Dorothea Tanning. 115 ill. 1966 $9.00

Brancusi: His Early Works: 1905-1908, by Geo. Bogza, ill. 1965 $10.00

Brandi (Cesare) *Burri*. 134 ill., folio, boxed 1964 $40.00

Branner (Robert) *La Cathedrale de Bourges et sa Place dans l'Architecture Gothique*. 138 ill. 1962 $10.00.

Brenson (Theodore) *Light into Color, Light into Space*. 15 ill. 1959 $2.50

Brongers (Georg A.) *Nicotiana Tabacum. The History of Tobacco Smoking in the Netherlands*. 167 ill., some in color, bibliog., 1964 $12.50

Bufano (Beniamino) *American Sculptor*. vol. 1 122 ill. 1957 $17.50
    vol. 2 in preparation, ready end of 1967

Bullrich (Francisco) *Arquitectura Argentina Contemporanea*. 300 ill. 1964 $7.00

(Le) Cabinet Fantastique
    Vol. 1: *Projets et Divagations de C. N. Ledoux, Architecte du Roi*, French text by Y. Christ. 80 ill. 1961 $10.00
    Vol. 2: *Didier Barra et Francois de Nome dits, Monsu Desiderio*, French text by Dr. Felix Sluys. 114 ill. 1961 $12.50
    Vol. 3: *Victor Hugo Dessinateur*, by Gaetan Picon. 250 ill 1964 $15.00
    Vol. 4: *Bresdin*, by Claude Roger-Marx. 264 ill., 1966 $15.00

Callery (Mary) *Sculpture*. 172 ill. 1961 $15.00

Campigli (Massimo) *Scrupules*. 117 ill. 1957 $9.50

Carli (Enzo) *Il Duomo di Orvieto*. 267 ill. 1965 $67.50

Carver (Norman F.) *Silent Cities of Mexico and the Maya*. 170 ill., 16 drawings, 1965 $20.00

Ceroni (Ambrogio) *Modigliani: Dessins, Sculptures*. 222 ill. 1965 $15.00

Chermayeff (Ivan) *Blind Mice and Other Numbers*. over 50 ill. 1961 $3.50

Cirlot (Juan-Eduardo) *Lucio Fontana*. 37 ill. 1966 $4.00

Coburn (Alvin Langdon) *A Portfolio*. 16 ill. limited ed. 1962 $12.50

Cossio del Pomar (Felipe) *Peruvian Colonial Art: The Cuzco School of Painting*. 65 ill. 18 color plates, 1965 $10.00

Crispolti (E. and G. Marchiori) *Corrado Cagli*. 268 ill., 88 color plates, 1964 $37.50

Cuevas by Cuevas. 100 ill. 1965 $5.00

(The) Dada Movement (Galleria Schwarz, Milan)
    1. *Arman, Raysse, Spoerri, Dufrene, Rotelfo, Villegle*. 94 ill. 1966 $1.50
    2. *Dada in Italy*. in prep. 1966 $1.50
    3. *'Round the World with Dada*. in prep. 1966 $1.50
    4. *The Protagonists: Dada is 50 Years Young*. in prep. 1966 $1.50
    5. *Towards a Cold Poetic Image*. in prep. 1966 $1.50

De Angelis D'Ossat (G. and C. Pietrangeli) *Il Campidoglio di Michelangelo*. 49 ill., over 100 drawings, plans, 1965 $95.00

De Bock (Paul Aloise) *Paul Delvaux: Der Mensch, Der Maler*. 56 ill. 1965 $8.50

Other Books published or distributed by George Wittenborn, Inc.

1018 Madison Avenue, New York, N. Y. 10021
and 91 Montgomery Street, Scarsdale, N. Y. 10583

Degas (Edgar) *Huit Sonnets*. 19 ill. 1947 $4.00
Denby (Edwin) *Mediterranean Cities*. 30 ill. 1956 $7.50
Dereux (Philippe) *Raymond Grandjean*. 10 ill. 1959 $2.50
Deroudille (Rene) *Rene Laubies*. French text 10 ill. 1957 $3.00
Documenti D'Arte D'Oggi, Ed. by the mac espace group in Milan, Italy
      Vol. 3 1955-1956, 110 ill. $12.50
      Vol. 4 1956-1957, 160 ill. $12.50
      Vol. 5 1957-1958, 100 ill. $12.50
Documents of Modern Art Series. See: Cover page
Dooijes (D. and P. Brattinga) *History of the Dutch Poster*. 350 ill. 1966   c. $28.00
Due Dimensioni. A dictionary of contemporary Italian commercial designers, text in 4 languages,
      edited by Max Huber et al, 2700 ill. 1965 $30.00
Duthuit (Georges) *Le Serpent dans la Galere*. 34 ill. 1945 $15.00
Far Eastern Antiquities Museum, Stockholm. Details on request
      Bulletin No. 36, 250 pp., 75 ill. 1964 $14.75
      Bulletin No. 37, 254 pp., 81 ill. 1965 $14.75
(Le) Fauconnier. Text by Ozenfant, ed. by J. B. Neumann, 9 ill. 1949 $1.00
Feldman (Eugene) *New York: West Side*. Fold-out plate in end boards, limited ed. 1965 $50.00
Focillon (Henri *The Life of Forms In Art*. 19 ill. reprint 1966 $2.50
Four Great Makers of Modern Architecture. Gropius, Le Corbusier, Mies van der Rohe, Wright. Sym-
      posium held at Columbia University School of Architecture in 1961. 1964 $7.50
Gallatin (A. E.) *Paintings of A. E. Gallatin*. 40 ill. 1948 $2.50
Gangoly (O. C.) *Indian Terracotta Art*. 50 ill. 1959 $9.00
Gasparini (Graziano)
      La Arquitectura Colonial de Coro. ill. 1961 $20.00
      La Arquitectura Colonial en Venezuela. ill. 1965 $30.00
      La Casa Colonial Venezolana. 149 ill. 1962 $7.50
Gaudi (Antonio) Preface by Le Corbusier. 61 ill. 1958 $7.50
George (Waldemar) *Hilaire Hiler and Structuralism: New Concept of Form-Color*. 8 ill. 1958 $2.50
Gindertall (R. V.) *Morice Lipsi*. 104 ill. 1965 $15.00
Gleizes (Albert) *Le Cubisme 1908-1914. Cahiers*. Vol. 1: *Souvenirs*. ill. 1957 $3.00
Goeritz. *Mathias Goeritz*, by Olivia Zuniga. 190 ill. 1963 $7.00

Green (Samuel Adams) *Andy Warhol*. 27 ill. 1965 $7.50

Gregory (Albert) *Color in Line*. 16 ill., limited ed. 1960 $40.00

Haass (Terry and Ferrand, Michel) *Germinal*. 6 orig. color etchings. 1957 $100.00

Hammer (Victor) *Memory and Her Nine Daughters*. 1957 $15.00

Henze (Anton) *La Tourette: The Le Corbusier Monastery*. 48 photos by B. Moosbrugger, 1966 $4.50

Herzka (Dorothy) *Pop Art*. 27 ill. 1965 $3.00

Honegger (Gottfried) *Fiktion und Realitat erster Versuch einer Zusammenfassung meines heutigen Stand-ortes in 24 Texten*. 5 orig. lithographs. 1956 $25.00

Honegger-Lavater (Warja) Folded stories. Original lithographs in numbered editions.

> 2. *Die Grille und die Ameise* (The Grasshopper and the Ant) $3.50
>
> 3. *Match* $3.50
>
> 4. *Die Party* $3.50
>
> 5. *La Promenade en Ville* $3.50
>
> 6. *Rape of the Sabines* $3.75
>
> 7. *Passion and Reason* $3.75
>
> 8. *The Good Intention is Blue* $4.50
>
> 9. *Night and Day and Night . . . and Day and Night* $4.50
>
> 10. *Extra-ordinary Lemuel* $4.50

Hostettler (Rudolf) *Technical Terms of the Printing Industry*. 3rd rev. ed. 200 ill. 1959 $4.00

Howarth (Thomas) *Charles Rennie Mackintosh and the Modern Movement*. 250 ill. 1953 $12.50

Ioannou (A. S.) *Byzantine Frescoes of Euboea*. Vol. 1 100 ill. 1959 $10.00

Jenkins (Paul) *Seeing Voice, Welsh Heart*. 17 poems by Cyril Hodges, 6 original color lithos, limited ed., 1965 $150.00

Kahn (Louis I.) *The Notebooks and Drawings of Louis I. Kahn*. over 100 ill. 1962 $14.50

Kahnweiler (D. H.) *Pour Daniel-Henry Kahnweiler*. 42 ill., 8 color lithos by Mourlot, 1965 $35.00

Kent (Adaline) *Autobiography*. 78 ill. 1958 $5.00

Kinetic Art. Four essays by Stephen Bann, Reg Gadney, Frank Popper and Philip Steadman. 80 ill. 1966 $3.00

Le Corbusier *Complete Works*. 1910-1960 800 ill. reprint ready 1967

> Vol. 1:   1910-1929, 400 ill. 1960 $15.00
>
> Vol. 2:   1929-1934, 400 ill. 1964 $15.00
>
> Vol. 3:   1934-1938, 400 ill. 1964 $15.00
>
> Vol. 4:   1938-1946, 400 ill. 1961 $15.00
>
> Vol. 5:   1946-1952, 400 ill. 1955 $15.00
>
> Vol. 6:   1952-1957, 500 ill. 1957 $15.00
>
> Vol. 7:   1957-1962, 500 ill. 1965 $18.50

Other Books published or distributed by George Wittenborn, Inc.

1018 Madison Avenue, New York, N. Y. 10021
and 91 Montgomery Street, Scarsdale, N. Y. 10583

Lehmbruck. *Die Druckgraphik von Wilhelm Lehmbruck,* by Erwin Petermann. 239 ill. 1964 $45.00
(Louise) Leiris Gallery Exhibition Catalogues, ill.
Series A:
1. *Pablo Picasso: Peintures, 1955-1956* $3.50
2. *Andre Masson: Peintures recentes et anciennes* $4.50
3. *A Beaudin: Peintures, 1927-1957* $2.50
4. *Juan Gris: Peintures de 1926 et 1927* $4.50
5. *E. de Kermadec: Peintures 1927-56* $4.50
6. *Fernand Leger: Dessins et Gouaches* $4.50
7. *Suzanne Roger: Peintures 1923-1958* $2.50
8. *Henri Laurens: Sculptures en pierre* $2.50
9. *Elie Lascaux: Peintures 1921-1959* $4.50
10. *Picasso: Les Menines 1957* $4.50
11. *Picasso: 45 gravures sur linoleum, 1958-1960* $4.50
12. *Picasso: Dessins 1959-1960* $3.50
13. *Y. Rouvre: Peintures 1951-1961* $2.50
14. *Picasso: Peintures (Vauvenargues 1959-1961)* $4.50
15. *A. Masson: Peintures 1960-1961* $4.50
16. *Picasso: "Dejeuner sur l'Herbe" de Manet* $4.50
17. *Picasso: Peintures 1962-1963* (now out of print)
Series B:
1. *D.-H. Kahnweiler: 50 Ans d'Edition* $3.50
2. *A. Masson: Dessins, 1960* $2.50
3. *Manolo: Sculptures-Gouaches-Dessins* $4.50
5. *Juan Gris: Dessins* $4.50
6. *Henri Laurens: Terre-Cuites (Clay Sculptures)* $2.50
7. *A. Beaudin: Sculptures* $2.50
Lewis (David) *Mondrian. His Paintings.* 10 ill. 1957 $2.50
Constantin Brancusi. 65 ill. 1958 $3.50
Leymarie (Jean) *Marc Chagall Monotypes, 1961-1965.* 25 color ill., limited ed. 1966 $42.50
Macagy (Douglas) *James Boynton.* 14 ill. 1959 $3.95
Madsen (Stephan Tschudi) *Munch's Wall Paintings.* 13 ill. 1959 $1.00

Maechler (Rene and Georges Thonet) *Paesaggi di Donna*. 35 photographs of the nude, 1965 $12.50
Marchiori (Giuseppe) *Jean Arp 1913-1963*. 95 ill. 1963 $20.00
Marchiori (Giuseppe) *Quinto Ghermandi*. 45 ill. 1962 $4.50
Masson (Andre) *Mythology of Being*. limited ed. 9 ill. portfolio. 1942 $25.00
              Nocturnal Notebook 16 ill. 1944 $3.00
Mathieu (Georges) *From the Abstract to The Possible*. 21 ill. 1960 $3.50
Medieval Wooden Sculpture in Sweden
        Vol. 1: *Attitudes to the Heritage*. ill. 1964 $8.50
        Vol. 2: *Romanesque and Gothic Sculpture*. ill. 1966 $9.50
        Vol. 3: *Late Medieval Sculpture*. ill. 1966 $9.50
        Vol. 4: *Catalogue*. ill. 1966 $17.50
        Vol. 5: *Plates*. 1964 $35.00
Mercandino (Cesare) *Impianti Sportivi*. 2 vols., ill. 1965 $40.00
Miranda (Salvador) *Les Palais des Empereurs Byzantins*. 34 ill., limited ed. 1965 $10.00
Modern Artists In America, Ed. by R. Motherwell, Ad Reinhardt, B. Karpel. 160 ill. 1952 $8.50
Monet (Claude) by Adrian Stokes, 8 color plates. 1958 $2.50
Moore (Henry) *Sculpture & Drawings:*
        Vol. 1. 1921-1948. 254 ill. 1957 $15.00
        Vol. 2. 1949-1954. 195 ill. reprint, 1965 $15.00
        Vol. 3. 1955-1964. 148 ill. 1965 $15.00
                Stone and Wood Carvings 1922-1961. 57 ill. 1961 $4.00
Moscanyi (Paul) *Karl Knaths*. 60 ill. 1958 $5.00
Mroszczak (Jozef) *Polnische Plakatkunst* (The Polish Poster In Art) 377 ill. 1962 $16.50
Muehsam (Alice) *German Readings 2: A Brief survey of art from the middle ages to the twentieth
        century for students of German and fine arts*. 2nd rev. ed. 1965 $3.50
Munari (Bruno) *The Circle*. ill. 1966 $4.50
                The Square. ill. reprint 1966 $4.50
                Good Design. ill. 1964 $1.50
New Furniture
        Vol. 4: 1956-1958. 347 ill. 1958 $12.50
Novelli (Gastone) *Antologia del Possibile*. ill. 1962 $4.00
Of Art, Plato To Picasso. Ed. by A. E. Gallatin. 3 ill. 1963 $2.00
Otto (Frei) *Zugbeanspruchte Konstruktionen* (Shell Constructions)
        Vol. 1: *Pneumatische Konstruktionen Berechnung der Membranen, Zugverankerungen im Bau-
                grund*. ill. 1962 $38.50

Other Books published or distributed by George Wittenborn, Inc.

1018 Madison Avenue, New York, N. Y. 10021
and 91 Montgomery Street, Scarsdale, N. Y. 10583

Vol. 2: *Grundbegriffe und Uebersicht der Konstrucktionen, Berechnung von Seilen, Seilnetzen und Seilwerken.* ill. 1966 $25.00

Vol. 3: *Spannweiten, Ideen und Versuche zum Leichtbau.* Ein Werkstattbericht von Conrad Roland. ill. 1965 $15.00

Picasso (Pablo) *Guernica.* 33 ill. 1956 $1.50

Lithographs 1945-1948. 67 ill. 1948 $3.00

Pirelli (Giulia and Carlo Orsi) *Milano.* 54 photos. 1965 $15.00

Ponente (Nello) *Mastroianni.* ill., limited ed., 1963 $27.50

(Les) Primitifs Flamands

Vol. 4: *New England Museums,* by Colin T. Eisler. ill. 1961 $13.50

Vol. 5: *Le Musee National de Louvre,* by Helene Adhemar. ill. 1962 $15.50

Vol. 6: *La Chapelle Royale de Grenada,* by Roger von Schoute. ill. 1963 $18.50

Vol. 7: *Le Palais Ducal D'Urbin,* by Jacques Lavalleye. ill. 1964 $20.00

Vol. 8: *Le Musee de l'Ermitage,* by Vladimir Loewinson-Lessing and Nicolas Nicouline. ill. 1965 $17.50

Vol. 9: *Les Musees de Pologne.* in prep. 1966

Problems of Contemporary Art Series. See: Cover page

Rand (Paul) *Trademarks.* 1960 $10.00

Thoughts On Design. 94 ill. $15.00

Read (Herbert) *Kandinsky 1866-1944.* 8 ill. 1959 $2.50

Redig de Campos (D.) *Raffaello Nelle Stanze.* 73 color plates, 1965 $45.00

Rety (Louis) *Fely Mouttet, Peintre.* 12 ill. 1958 $2.00

Reynal (Jeanne) *The Mosaics of Jeanne Reynal.* 81 ill. 1964 $15.00

Richter (Hans and Herbert Read) *Hans Richter.* 144 ill. 1965 $19.50

Rodin, (Auguste) *A la Venus de Milo.* Fr. text. 6 ill. 1945 $4.00

Roesch (Kurt) 9 Engravings to accompany "The Sonnets to Orpheus" by Rainer Maria Rilke. 35 numbered and signed copies. 1944 $250.00

Rosenthal (Erwin) *The Changing Concept of Reality in Art.* 46 ill. 1962 $6.50

Ruscha (Edward) *Twenty Six Gasoline Stations.* 26 photos, 1962 $3.00

Various Small Fires. 20 photos, 1964 $3.00

Some Los Angelos Apartments. 40 photos of exteriors, 1965 $3.00

Sauvage (Tristan) *Nuclear Art.* Essays, manifestoes, 213 ill. 1962 $17.50

Schoofs (Rudolf) *Engravings.* Vol. 1. 22 ill. 1960 $2.50

                Engravings. Vol. 2. 16 ill. 1963 $4.50

Seuphor (Michel) *Lee Hersch, Abstract Artist.* 12 ill. 1954 $2.50

Shorr (Dorothy C.) *The Christ Child in Devotional Images In Italy during the 14th Century.* 450 ill. 1953 $6.50

Stahly (Francois) *Francois Stahly.* 84 ill. 1962 $6.50

Steinberg (Leo) *Jasper Johns. A critical study.* 30 ill. 1963 $3.50

Sweeney (James Johnson) *Afro (Basaldella) Paintings, Gouaches, Drawings.* 34 ill. 1961 $20.00

        The Miro Atmosphere. 93 ill. 1959 $7.50

        Same, with one signed orig. color litho. $75.00

Taillandier (Yvon) *Creation Miro 1961.* 60 ill. 1962 $9.00

Tanguy (Yves) *Catalogue of the Paintings of Yves Tanguy.* 462 ill. 1963 $37.50

Tapie (Michel) *Antonio Tapies.* 46 photographs. 1959 $7.50

Tapies. *Antoni Tapies,* by Blai Bonet. Spanish text, ill. 1965 $54.50

            Observations. 8 ill. 1956 $3.50

            Claire Falkenstein. 19 ill. 1959 $5.50

Teshigahara (Sofu) *Portfolio.* 31 ill. $9.00

              Sculpture, 1957-58. 27 ill. $6.00

Trans/Formation: arts, communication, environment, Ed. by H. Holtzman

        Vol. 1, No. 1 1950 $3.50

        Vol. 1, No. 2 1951 $3.50

        Vol. 1, No. 3 1952 $3.50

Trucchi (Lorenzo) *Jean Dubuffet.* Italian text, 360 ill. 1965 $45.00

Tselos (Dimitri) *The Sources of the Utrecht Psalter Miniatures.* 361 ill. 1960 $20.00

Vasarely. *Victor Vasarely,* by Victor and Marcel Joray. ill. 1965 $27.50

Villani (D.) *Storia del Manifesto Pubblicitario.* History of the Poster. 900 ill. 1965 $36.00

Werbeform (German Graphic Annual).

        Vol. 3: German-Eng. text, 1000 ill. 1962 $20.00

Weston (Edward) *The Daybooks of Edward Weston.* Vol. 1: Mexico. 40 ill. 1962 $10.00

Wilke (Ulfert) *One, Two and More.* portfolio, limited ed. 1960 $20.00

           Fragments from Nowhere. 19 facsimiles. 1960 $20.00

Wurman (Richard Saul) *Various Dwellings Described in a Comparative Manner.* 35 drawings by students of University of North Carolina School of Design, 1964 $7.00

Young (Dennis and Barbara) *Furniture in Britain Today.* 310 ill. 1964 $10.50

Zannas (Eliky) *Khajuraho.* 176 ill. 1961 $47.50

Zekowski (Arlene) *Concretions.* 13 ill. by Milton Avery, limited edition. 1962 $5.00

            Abraxas. 8 woodcuts by Herman Zaage, 1964 $5.00